THE BEATLF

HELP!

Wise Publications
London/New York/Sydney/Paris

Exclusive Distributors:
Music Sales Limited
8/9 Frith Street,
London W1V 5TZ, England.
Music Sales Pty Limited
120 Rothschild Avenue,
Rosebery, NSW 2018,
Australia.

This book © Copyright 1992 by Wise Publications
Order No.NO90541
ISBN 0-7119-3265-4

Music arranged by Frank Booth
Music processed by MSS Studios
Book design by Pearce Marchbank Studio
Computer origination by Adam Hay

Music Sales' complete catalogue lists thousands of titles
and is free from your local music shop, or direct from
Music Sales Limited. Please send a cheque/postal order
for £1.50 for postage to: Music Sales Limited,
Newmarket Road, Bury St. Edmunds, Suffolk IP33 3YB.

Your Guarantee of Quality
As publishers, we strive to produce every book to the
highest commercial standards.
The music has been freshly engraved and the book has
been carefully designed to minimise awkward page turns
and to make playing from it a real pleasure.
Particular care has given to specifying acid-free,
neutral-sized paper which has not been chlorine bleached
but produced with special regard for the environment.
Throughout, the printing and binding have been planned
to ensure a sturdy, attractive publication which should
give years of enjoyment.
If your copy fails to meet our high standards,
please inform us and we will gladly replace it.

Printed in the United Kingdom by
Halstan & Co Limited, Amersham, Buckinghamshire.

HELP!

Words & Music by John Lennon & Paul McCartney.

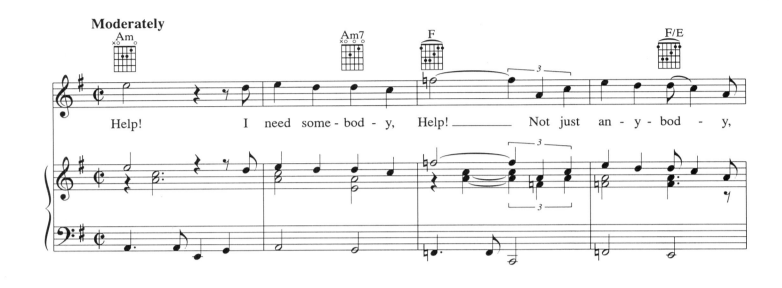

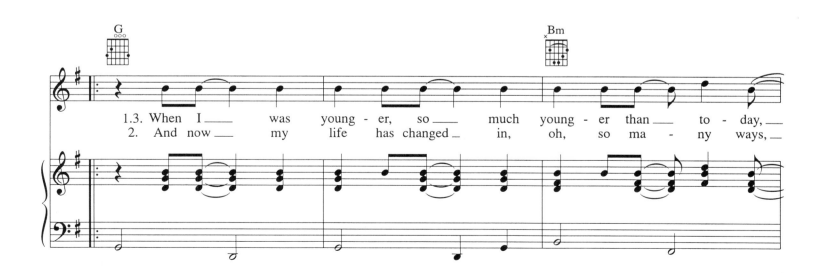

I nev-er need-ed an-y-bod-y's help in an-y way.
My in-de-pen-dence seems to van-ish in the haze.

But now these days are gone, I'm not so self-as-sured,
But ev-'ry now and then I feel so in-se-cure,

Now I find I've changed my mind, I've
I know that I just need you like I've

o-pened up the doors.
nev-er done be-fore.

Help me if you can, I'm feel-ing

YOU'VE GOT TO HIDE YOUR LOVE AWAY

Words & Music by John Lennon & Paul McCartney.
© Copyright 1965 Northern Songs, under license to
MCA Music Limited, 77 Fulham Palace Road, London W6.
All Rights Reserved. International Copyright Secured.

1. Here I stand with head in hand,
2. How can I ev - en try?

turn my face to the wall.
I can nev - er win.

If she's gone I
Hear - ing them,

can't go on
see - ing them

feel - ing two feet small.
in the state I'm in.

THE NIGHT BEFORE

Words & Music by John Lennon & Paul McCartney.

Moderately

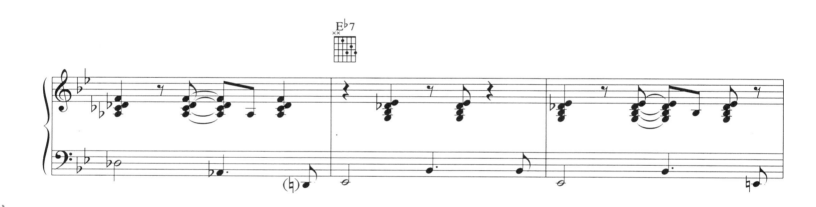

1. We said our ___ good - byes, ___
2. Were you tell - ing lies? ___

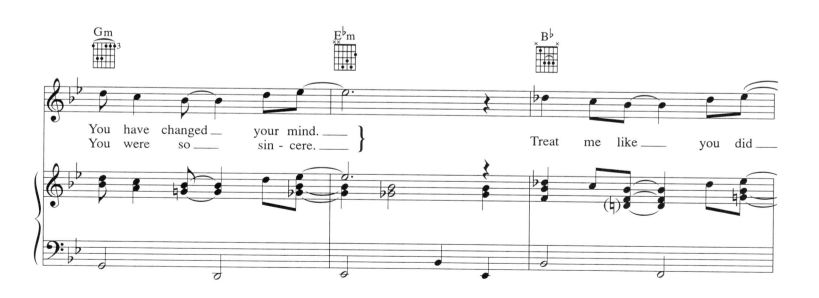

13

I NEED YOU

Words & Music by George Harrison.

1. You don't re - a - lize how much I need you,
2. Said you had a thing or two to tell me.
3. Please re - mem - ber how I feel a - bout you,

Love you all the time and nev - er leave you.
How was I to know you would up - set me?
I could nev - er real - ly live with - out you;

YOU'RE GOING TO LOSE THAT GIRL

Words & Music by John Lennon & Paul McCartney.

You're gon - na lose that girl. ___ You're gon - na

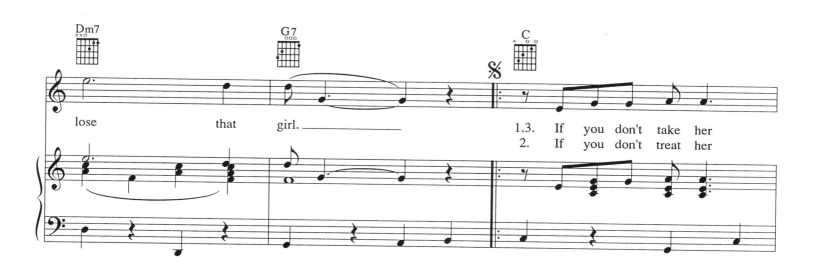

lose that girl. ___

1.3. If you don't take her
2. If you don't treat her

out to - night, ___ she's gon - na change her mind. ___
right my friend, ___ you're gon - na find her gone. ___

To Coda⊕

And I will take her out to-night __ and I will treat her kind. __
'Cause I will treat her right. and then __ you'll be the lone-ly one. __

You're gon-na lose that girl. __ You're gon-na

lose that girl. __ girl. __ You're gon-na

lose. __ I'll make a point of

ANOTHER GIRL

Words & Music by John Lennon & Paul McCartney.
© Copyright 1965 Northern Songs, under license to
MCA Music Limited, 77 Fulham Palace Road, London W6.
All Rights Reserved. International Copyright Secured.

Steady 2 beat

For I have got _____ an-oth-er girl, _____ an-oth-er girl, _____

1. You're mak-in' me say _____ that I've _____ got no-bod-y but you.
2. She's sweet-er than all _____ the girls _____ and I've met _____ quite a few.
3,4. I don't wan-na say _____ that I've _____ been un-hap-py with you;

But as _____ from to-day, well I've _____ got some-bod-y that's new.
No-bod-y in all the world _____ can do what _____ she can do.
But as _____ from to-day, well I've _____ seen some-bod-y that's new.

I ain't _____ no fool, and I _____ don't take what I _____ don't want. For I have got _____
And so I'm tell-ing you, _____ This time you'd bet-ter
I ain't no fool, and I _____ don't take what I _____ don't

Tacet

TICKET TO RIDE

Words & Music by John Lennon & Paul McCartney.

Moderate rock tempo

think I'm gon-na be sad. ___ I think it's to-day, ___ yeh! ___
(2) said that liv-ing with me ___ is bring-ing her down, ___ yeh! ___

The girl that's driv-ing me mad ___ is go-ing a-way. ___
For she would nev-er be free ___ when I was a-round. ___

ACT NATURALLY

Words by Vonnie Morrison. Music by Johnny Russell.

Moderately

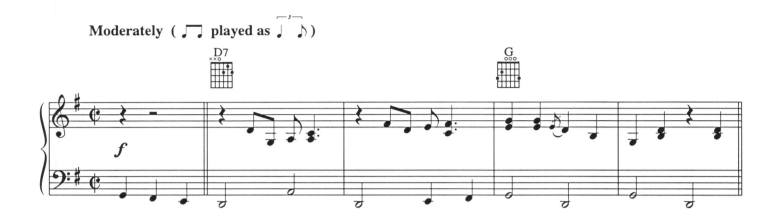

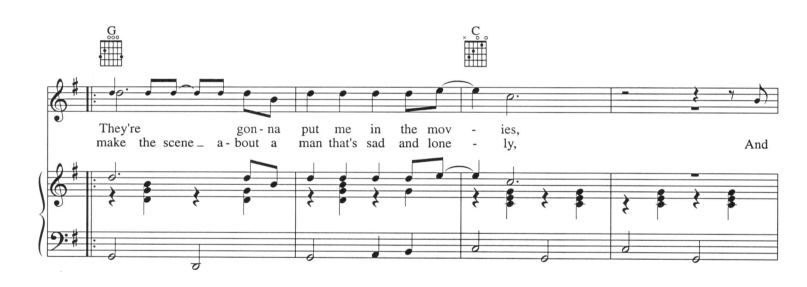

They're   gon - na   put me   in the mov -   ies,
make the scene   a - bout a   man that's sad and lone -   ly,   And

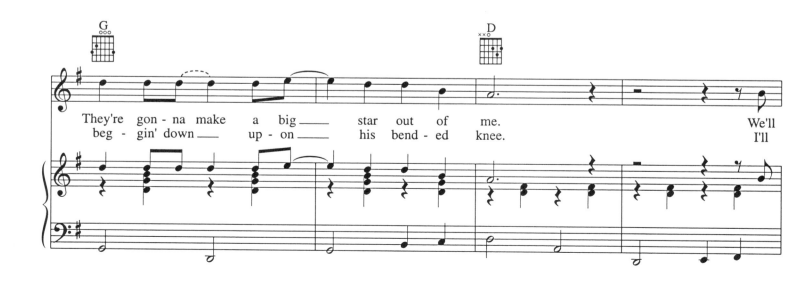

They're   gon - na make   a   big   star out of   me.   We'll
beg - gin' down   up - on   his bend - ed   knee.   I'll

make a film ___ a-bout a man that's sad and lone - ly,
play the part, ___ but I won't need re-hears - in';

And

all I got-ta do is act nat - 'ral-ly.
All I have to do is act nat - 'ral-ly.

Well, I

bet you I'm gon-na be a big ___ star,

might

win an "Os - car", you can ___ nev-er tell, ___

The

27

movies gonna make me a big___ star 'cause

I can play the part___ so well.___ Well, I

hope you come and see me in the mov - ies,

Then I'll know___ that you___ will plain - ly see The

28

big- gest fool __ that ev - er hit the big __ time.

And all I got - ta do is act nat - 'ral - ly.

(2) We'll

IT'S ONLY LOVE

Words & Music by John Lennon & Paul McCartney.

Moderately

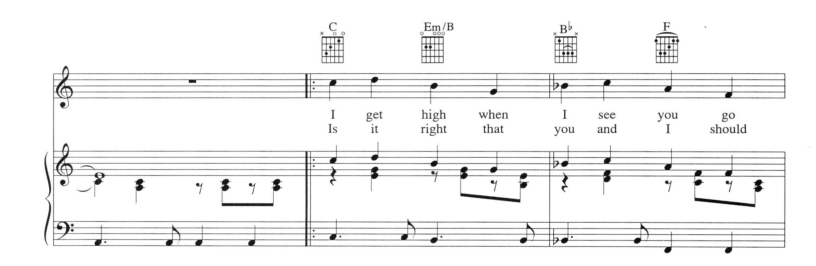

I get high when I see you go
Is it right right when that you and I go should

by. My, oh my! when you sigh, my
fight ev - 'ry night? Just the sight of

YOU LIKE ME TOO MUCH

Words & Music by George Harrison.

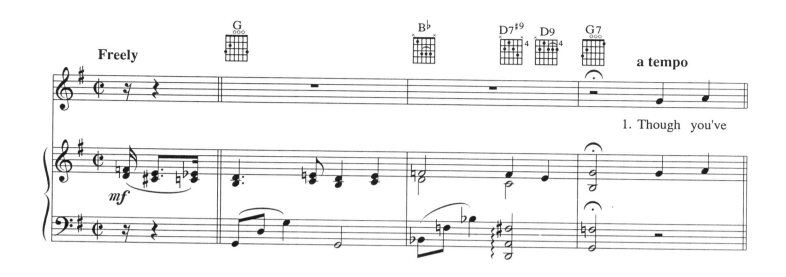

Freely   a tempo

1. Though you've

gone a - way ___ this morn - ing, you'll ___ be back ___ a - gain ___ to - night,
(2) tried be - fore ___ to leave ___ me but ___ you have - n't got ___ the nerve
3. I will fol - low you ___ and bring ___ you back ___ where you ___ be - long, ___

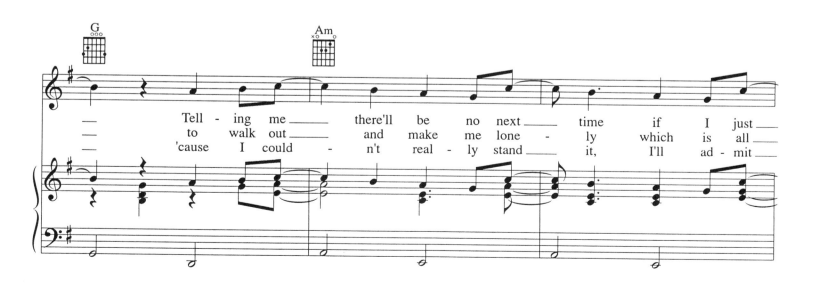

— Tell - ing me ___ there'll be no next ___ time if I just ___
— to walk out ___ and make me lone - ly which is all ___
— 'cause I could - n't real - ly stand ___ it, I'll ad - mit ___

TELL ME WHAT YOU SEE

Words & Music by John Lennon & Paul McCartney.

Moderately

1. If you let ___ me take ___
2. Big and black ___ the clouds ___
3. Lis - ten to ___ me one ___

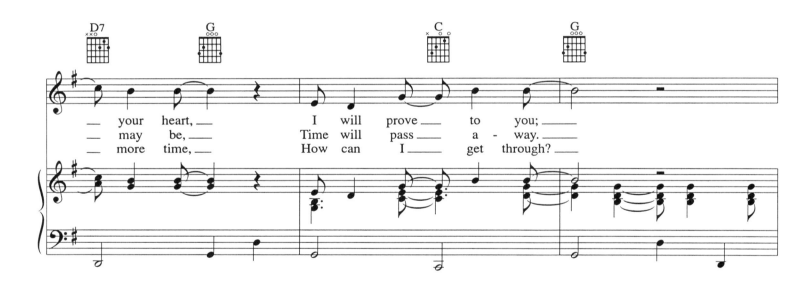

___ your heart, ___   I will prove ___ to you; ___
___ may be, ___   Time will pass ___ a - way. ___
___ more time, ___   How can I ___ get through? ___

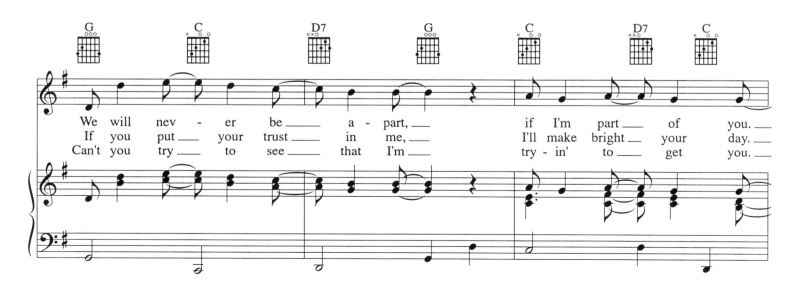

We will nev - er be ___ a - part, ___   if I'm part ___ of you.
If you put ___ your trust ___ in me, ___   I'll make bright ___ your day.
Can't you try ___ to see ___ that I'm ___   try - in' to ___ get you.

I'VE JUST SEEN A FACE

Words & Music by John Lennon & Paul McCartney.
© Copyright 1965 Northern Songs, under license to
MCA Music Limited, 77 Fulham Palace Road, London W6.
All Rights Reserved. International Copyright Secured.

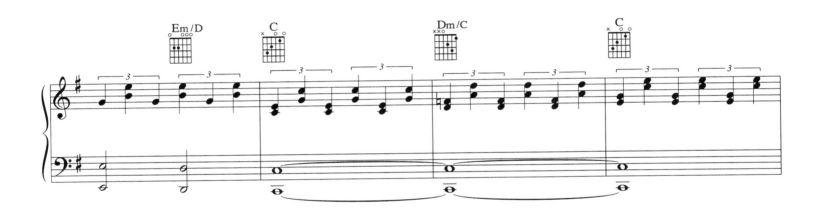

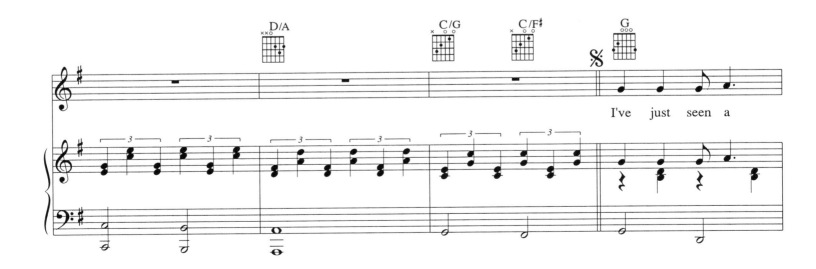

I've just seen a

YESTERDAY

Words & Music by John Lennon & Paul McCartney.

Moderately, with expression

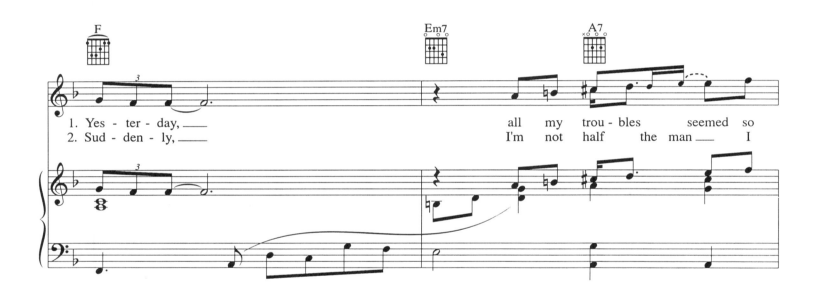

1. Yes - ter - day, ___ all my trou - bles seemed so
2. Sud - den - ly, ___ I'm not half the man ___ I

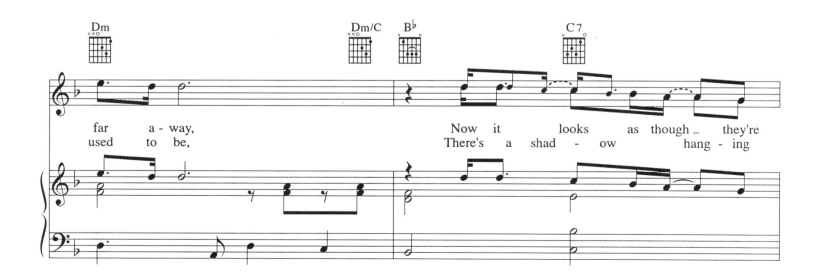

far a - way,
used to be,

Now it looks as though ___ they're
There's a shad - ow hang - ing

DIZZY MISS LIZZIE

Words & Music by Larry Williams.

1. You make me diz-zy, Miss ___ Liz - zie, ___ the way you rock and roll. ___
2. You make me diz-zy, Miss ___ Liz - zie, ___ when you call my name. ___
3. Run and tell your ma - ma I want you to be my bride. ___

The Beatles

Enya

Phil Collins

Van Morrison

Bob Dylan

Sting

Paul Simon

Tracy Chapman

Eric Clapton

Pink Floyd

New Kids On The Block

Bryan Adams

Tina Turner

Elton John

Bee Gees

Whitney Houston

AC/DC

Bringing you the words

All the latest in rock and pop. Plus the brightest and best in West End show scores. Music books for every instrument under the sun. And exciting new teach-yourself ideas like "Let's Play Keyboard" - in cassette/book packs, or on video. Available from all good music shops.

and music

Music Sales' complete catalogue lists thousands of titles and is available free from your local music shop, or direct from Music Sales Limited. Please send a cheque or postal order for £1.50 (for postage) to:

Music Sales Limited
Newmarket Road,
Bury St Edmunds,
Suffolk IP33 3YB

Buddy

Five Guys Named Moe

Les Misérables

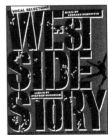
West Side Story

Phantom Of The Opera

Show Boat

The Rocky Horror Show

Bringing you the world's best music.